by **JIM APPLEGATE**
illustrated by **MACAYLA MURILLO**

MARRY A MAN LIKE ME

LUCIDBOOKS

Marry a Man like Me

As a dad, I wanted to know who I needed to be for my daughters. I wanted to have a goal to achieve so that I could say, "I'm doing okay at this dad thing" or "I realize I could improve in this area." As my daughters grew older and started dating, though, I realized I also wanted them to know what to look for in the guys they were willing to spend time with. "Is he cute?" is a great question to ask, but it is not a characteristic that will lead to happily ever after. Reading this book to your daughter will help with both of these dilemmas. First, you'll know as a dad what your daughter needs in you and how you can measure success. Second, your daughter will have a list of characteristics that she will use to measure the men she dates, a list that will help her make great decisions about whom she will eventually marry.

This book will be convicting to each dad who reads it to his daughter. But instead of living in condemnation because you cannot be perfect, make sure you read the page at the end of the book that points you back to the good news of Jesus for both you and your daughter.

I'm the proud dad of four beautiful daughters, and this book is dedicated to each one of them.

~ Jim

This book is part of the *Like Me* series. Other titles in this series include:
Be a Man like Me
Marry a Lady like Me
Be a Lady like Me

For more information, check out www.belikeme.org

Marry a man like me...
A man who wants to have fun with you,
just like I do

A man who is kind to you,
just like I am

Marry a man like me. . .
A man who protects you,
just like I do

A man who is proud of you,
just like I am

Marry a man like me. . .
A man who says he's sorry,
just like I do

A man who knows you are beautiful,
just like I do

Marry a man like me. . .
**A man who listens to you,
just like I do**

A man who knows what you like,
just like I do

Marry a man like me. . .
A man who prays for you,
just like I do

A man who provides for you,
just like I do

Marry a man like me...
A man who wants to spend time with you,
just like I do

A man who points you to Jesus,
just like I do

Marry a man like me...
A man who teaches you about God's love,
just like I do

A man who cares for you,
just like I do

A man who cheers you on,
just like I do

Marry a man like me. . .

A man who knows that in order to be all of this for you, he needs Jesus,

just like I do.

To all the dads

If you're anything like me, you're probably squirming and feeling somewhat guilty while reading this book to your daughter, wishing you could embody all of these great characteristics for her. Let me offer you some help.

First, the only perfect father is our Heavenly Father. As you read this book, a great meditation is to think of how our Heavenly Father is all this to us. He is our provider, he loves to spend time listening to us, and he knows what we are good at. As I think about the stories in the gospels, I think about how Jesus displayed all the characteristics from this book to his disciples. Enjoy the way your Heavenly Father loves you. . .press deeper into the greatness of that relationship.

Second, remember that God's strength is revealed in our weakness (2 Corinthians 12:9). As you realize that you can't be everything you want to be for your daughter, your only option is to ask the Father for help and declare your absolute dependence on him. Our dependence actually brings him glory, and in turn brings us joy—win/win.

Third, it is important to live in confession to your daughter. Be honest and say, "I'm struggling to be this for you right now." It is important for her to hear your struggles because she too will struggle. Let your confession include, "That's why Daddy needs Jesus." In your confession of your weakness, show her your dependence on the perfect Father, and by this she will also learn to depend on the perfect Father. Your job is not to be the perfect dad—that is an impossible task—your job is to point your daughter to the perfect Dad and to show what it is to live in relationship with him.

One of my favorite passages of Scripture is Luke 11:11–13:

> *"What father among you, if his son asks for a fish, will instead of a fish give him a serpent; or if he asks for an egg, will give him a scorpion? If you then, who are evil, know how to give good gifts to your children, how much more will the heavenly Father give the Holy Spirit to those who ask him!"*

Just the fact that you are reading this book to your daughter is evidence that you love her and want what is best for her. As you consider how much you love your daughter and how much you want the best for her, think of how much more the heavenly Father loves you and is pouring out perfect blessings on you. Your biggest need as a dad is not to have more money, more wisdom, more knowledge, a better job, more time, or anything of the sort. Your biggest need is to know more of God's love and to have more of the Holy Spirit in your life. When you ask God to lead you, he gives you these gifts in abundance because he is your perfect Father. And, as you seek him, everything else falls into place (Matthew 6:33).

A dependent dad,
Jim

Jim Applegate is a pastor in Modesto, California. Before becoming a pastor, he spent twenty years in the construction industry. Jim has four daughters and one son, and has been married to his wife, Heather, for over twenty-five years.

www.belikeme.org

Macayla Murillo is an artist who lives in Modesto, California. She is married to her best friend, Bryan, and they are expecting their first child. Macayla loves to see the story of the gospel and the heart of our loving God exemplified through art.

CPSIA information can be obtained
at www.ICGtesting.com
Printed in the USA
BVHW020205250121
598664BV00012B/372